THE BLUES BROTHER

Production: Stephen Clark and Sadie Cook

Published 1994
Revised Edition 1997

IMP

© International Music Publications Limited
Griffin House, 161 Hammersmith Road, London W6 8BS, England

PETER GUNN THEME

By HENRY MANCINI

SHE CAUGHT THE KATY

Words and Music by
TAJ MAHAL and YANK RACHEL

GIMME SOME LOVIN'

Words and Music by STEVE WINWOOD,
MUFF WINWOOD and SPENCER DAVIS

Well, my tem - pera - ture's ris - ing and my feet left the floor,___

Well, my head's___ ex - plod - ing and I'm float - ing to sound,

Well, I feel so good everything is getting hot,
You'd better take some time off 'cos the place is on fire.
Better start baby, 'cos I have so much to do,
We made it baby, and it happened to you,
And I'm so glad we made it.
I want you, gimme some alovin', gimme some alovin',
Gimme some alovin', every day.

SHAKE A TAILFEATHER

Words and Music by
O HAYES, WILLIAMS and RICE

EVERYBODY NEEDS SOMEBODY TO LOVE

Words and Music by BERT BERNS,
SOLOMON BURKE and JERRY WEXLER

22

you, you, you. I need you, you, you. I need
(In the morn - ing)

to Coda ⊕

you, you when my soul's on fire.

Some - times I feel, I feel a lit - tle sad in - side.

The way my ba - by mis - treats me I'll ne - ver, ne - ver, ne - ver find a place to hide. I need

THINK

Words and Music by
TED WHITE and ARETHA FRANKLIN

THE OLD LANDMARK

Words and Music by
ADELINE BRUNNER

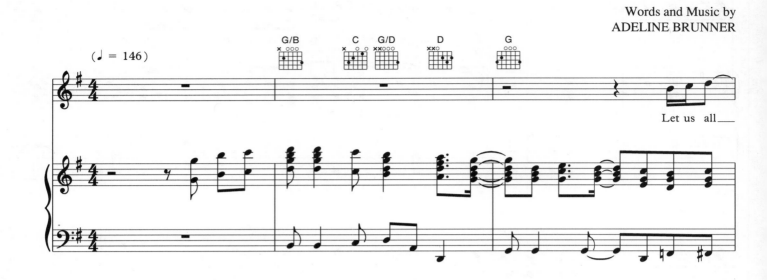

THEME FROM RAWHIDE

Words by NED WASHINGTON
Music by DIMITRI TIOMKIN

Roll-in' roll-in' roll-in'   roll-in' roll-in' roll-in'   roll-in' roll-in' roll-in'

roll-in' roll-in' roll-in' raw - hide._____

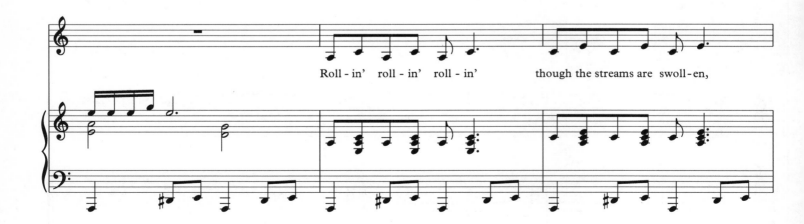

Roll-in' roll-in' roll-in'   though the streams are swoll-en,

39

MINNIE, THE MOOCHER

Words and Music by
CAB CALLOWAY and IRVING MILLS

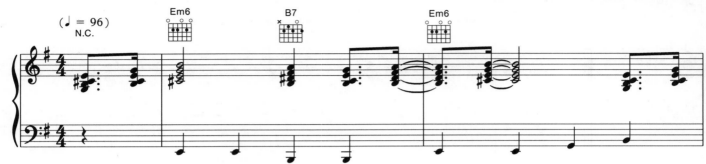

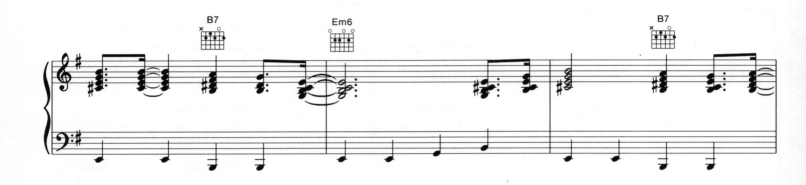

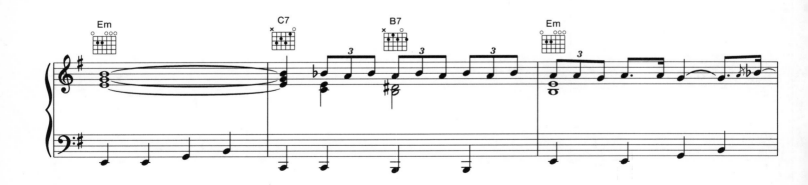

44

45

SWEET HOME CHICAGO

Words and Music by
HERMAN PARKER

-ca - go.____

JAILHOUSE ROCK

Words and Music by
JERRY LEIBER and MIKE STOLLER

4. The sad sack was a-sittin' on a block of stone,
   Way over in the corner weeping all alone.
   The warden said, 'Hey buddy, don't you be no square,
   If you can't find a partner, use a wooden chair!'
   Let's rock, etc.

5. Shiftly Henry said to Bugs, 'For Heaven's sake,
   No one's lookin', now's our chance to make a break.'
   Bugsy turned to Shifty and he said, 'Nix, nix,
   I wanna stick around a while and get my kicks.'
   Let's rock, etc.

You can be the featured soloist with
TAKE THE LEAD

Collect these titles, each with demonstration and full backing tracks on CD.

90s Hits

The Air That I Breathe (Simply Red)
Angels (Robbie Williams)
How Do I Live (LeAnn Rimes)
I Don't Want To Miss A Thing (Aerosmith)
I'll Be There For You (The Rembrandts)
My Heart Will Go On (Celine Dion)
Something About The Way
You Look Tonight (Elton John)
Frozen (Madonna)

Order ref: 6725A – Flute
Order ref: 6726A – Clarinet
Order ref: 6727A – Alto Saxophone
Order ref: 6728A – Violin

Movie Hits

Because You Loved Me (Up Close And Personal)
Blue Monday (The Wedding Singer)
(Everything I Do)
I Do It For You (Robin Hood: Prince Of Thieves)
I Don't Want To Miss A Thing (Armageddon)
I Will Always Love You (The Bodyguard)
Star Wars (Main Title) (Star Wars)
The Wind Beneath My Wings (Beaches)
You Can Leave Your Hat On (The Full Monty)

Order ref: 6908A – Flute
Order ref: 6909A – Clarinet
Order ref: 6910A – Alto Saxophone
Order ref: 6911A –Tenor Saxophone
Order ref: 6912A – Violin

TV Themes

Coronation Street
I'll Be There For You (theme from Friends)
Match Of The Day
(Meet) The Flintstones
Men Behaving Badly
Peak Practice
The Simpsons
The X-Files

Order ref: 7003A – Flute
Order ref: 7004A – Clarinet
Order ref: 7005A – Alto Saxophone
Order ref: 7006A – Violin

Christmas Songs

The Christmas Song
(Chestnuts Roasting On An Open Fire)
Frosty The Snowman
Have Yourself A Merry Little Christmas
Little Donkey
Rudolph The Red-Nosed Reindeer
Santa Claus Is Comin' To Town
Sleigh Ride
Winter Wonderland

Order ref: 7022A – Flute
Order ref: 7023A – Clarinet
Order ref: 7024A – Alto Saxophone
Order ref: 7025A – Violin
Order ref: 7026A – Piano
Order ref: 7027A – Drums

The Blues Brothers

She Caught The Katy And Left Me A
Mule To Ride
Gimme Some Lovin'
Shake A Tail Feather
Everybody Needs Somebody To Love
The Old Landmark
Think
Minnie The Moocher
Sweet Home Chicago

Order ref: 7079A - Flute
Order ref: 7080A - Clarinet
Order ref: 7081A - Alto Saxophone
Order ref: 7082A - Tenor Saxophone
Order ref: 7083A - Trumpet
Order ref: 7084A - Violin

Latin

Bailamos
Cherry Pink And
Apple Blossom White
Guantanamera
La Bamba
La Isla Bonita
Livin' La Vida Loca
Oye Mi Canto (Hear My Voice)
Soul Limbo

Order ref: 7259A - Flute
Order ref: 7260A - Clarinet
Order ref: 7261A - Alto Saxophone
Order ref: 7364A - Piano
Order ref: 7262A - Trumpet
Order ref: 7263A - Violin

Jazz

Birdland
Desafinado
Don't Get Around Much Anymore
Fascinating Rhythm
Misty
My Funny Valentine
One O'Clock Jump
Summertime

Order ref: 7124A - Flute
Order ref: 7173A - Clarinet
Order ref: 7174A - Alto Saxophone
Order ref: 7175A - Tenor Saxophone
Order ref: 7179A - Drums
Order ref: 7178A - Piano
Order ref: 7176A - Trumpet
Order ref: 7177A - Violin

Swing

Chattanooga Choo Choo
Choo Choo Ch'Boogie
I've Got A Gal In Kalamazoo
In The Mood
It Don't Mean A Thing
(If It Ain't Got That Swing)
Jersey Bounce
Pennsylvania 6-5000
A String Of Pearls

Order ref: 7235A - Flute
Order ref: 7236A - Clarinet
Order ref: 7237A - Alto Saxophone
Order ref: 7238A - Tenor Saxophone
Order ref: 7239A - Trumpet
Order ref: 7240A - Violin